W9-BKG-469

THE LAST FLOWER

A PARABLE IN PICTURES

THE LAST FLOWER

A PARABLE IN PICTURES

By

James Thurber

QUEENS HOUSE
Larchmont, New York 10538

TO THE READER

It is our pleasure to keep available uncommon titles and to this end, at the time of publication, we have used the best available sources. To aid catalogers and collectors, this title is printed in an edition limited to 300 copies. ——— **Enjoy!**

FOR ROSEMARY

IN THE WISTFUL HOPE THAT HER WORLD
WILL BE BETTER THAN MINE

THE LAST FLOWER

A PARABLE IN PICTURES

WORLD WAR XII, AS EVERYBODY KNOWS,

BROUGHT ABOUT THE COLLAPSE OF CIVILIZATION

TOWNS, CITIES, AND VILLAGES DISAPPEARED FROM THE EARTH

ALL THE GROVES AND FORESTS WERE DESTROYED

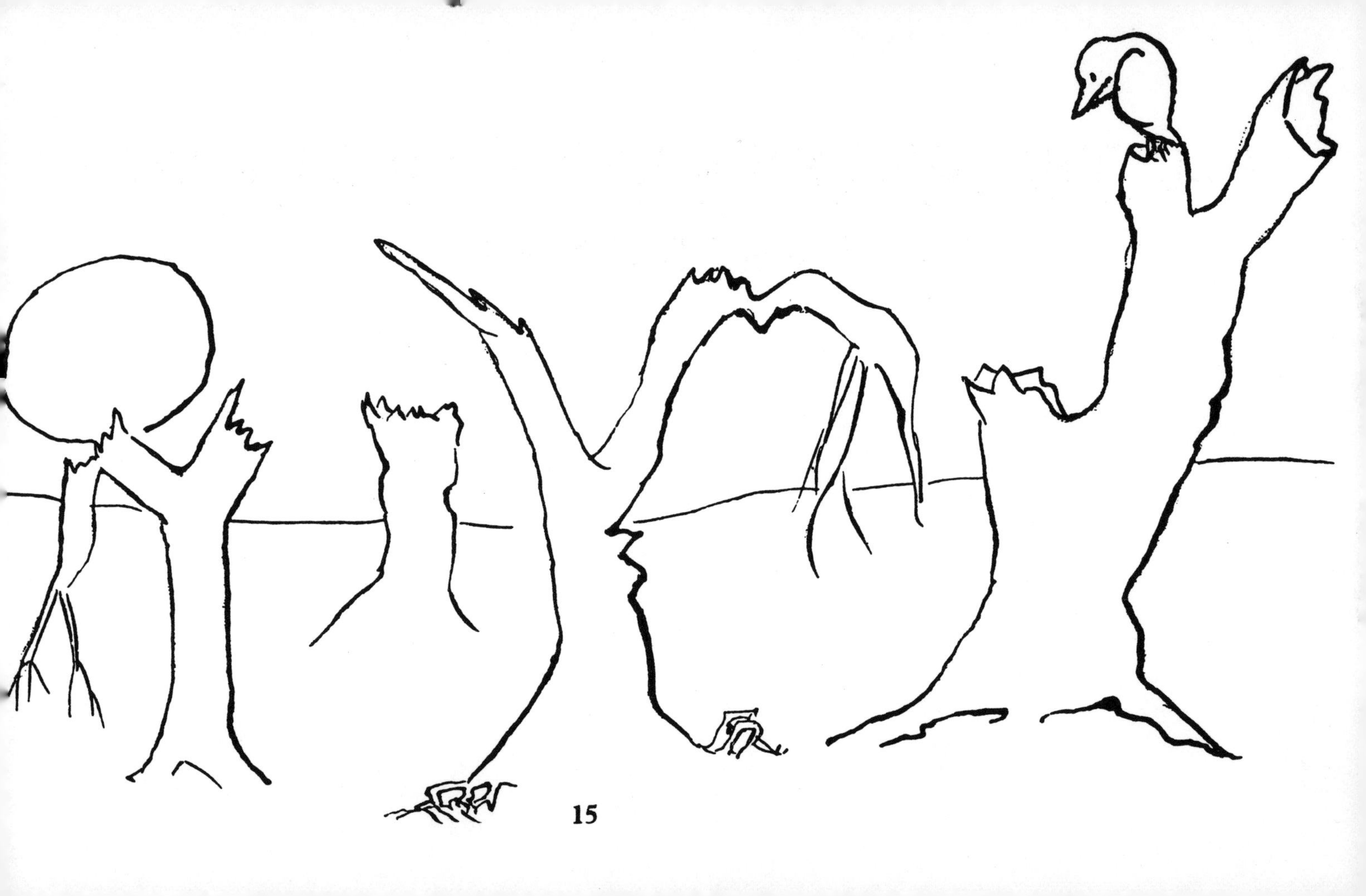

AND ALL THE GARDENS

AND ALL THE WORKS OF ART

DISCOURAGED AND DISILLUSIONED, DOGS DESERTED
THEIR FALLEN MASTERS

EMBOLDENED BY THE PITIFUL CONDITION
OF THE FORMER LORDS OF THE EARTH,
RABBITS DESCENDED UPON THEM

BOOKS, PAINTINGS, AND MUSIC DISAPPEARED
FROM THE EARTH, AND HUMAN BEINGS
JUST SAT AROUND, DOING NOTHING

YEARS AND YEARS WENT BY

EVEN THE FEW GENERALS WHO WERE LEFT
FORGOT WHAT THE LAST WAR HAD DECIDED

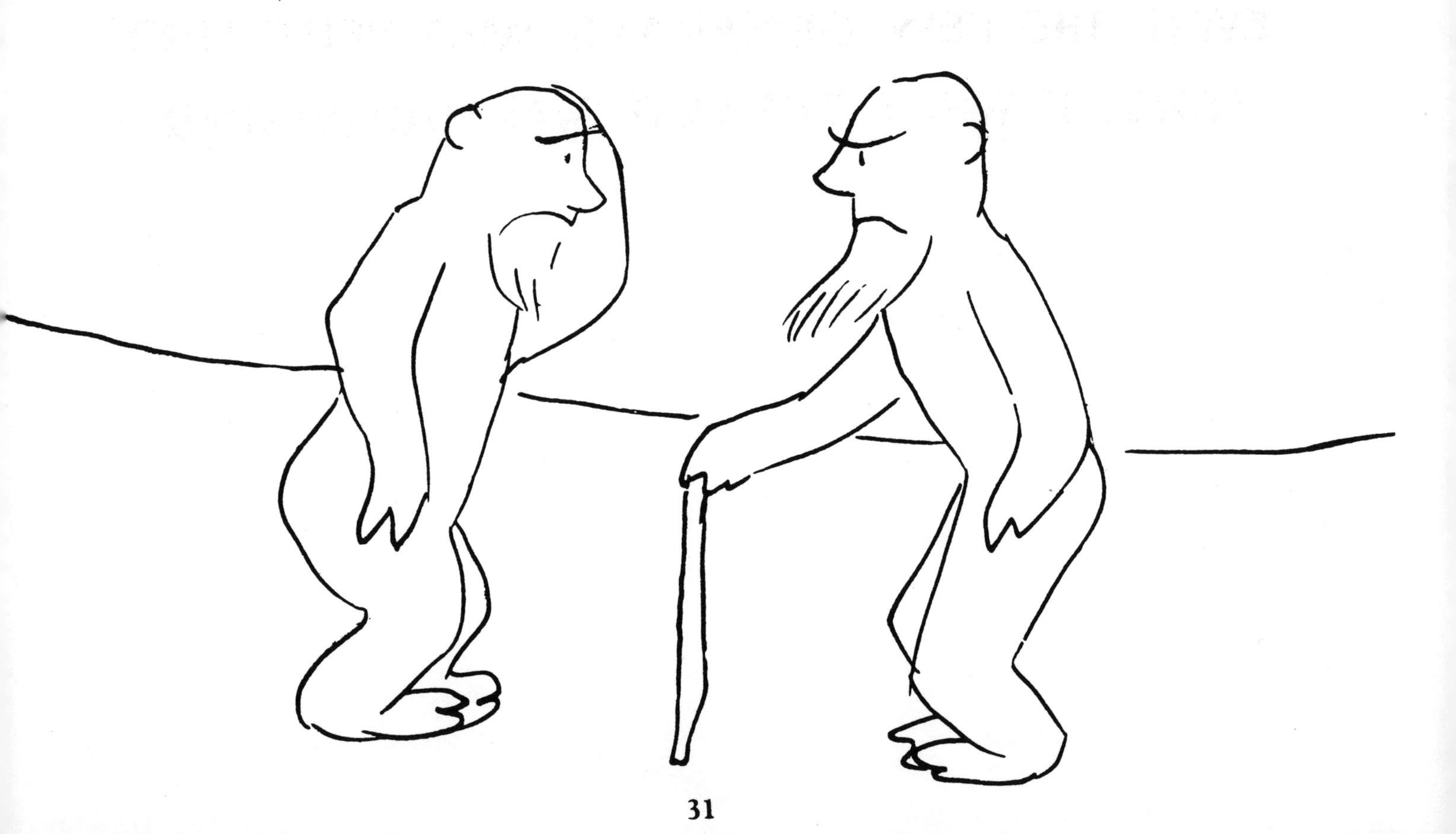

BOYS AND GIRLS GREW UP TO STARE AT EACH OTHER BLANKLY, FOR LOVE HAD PASSED FROM THE EARTH

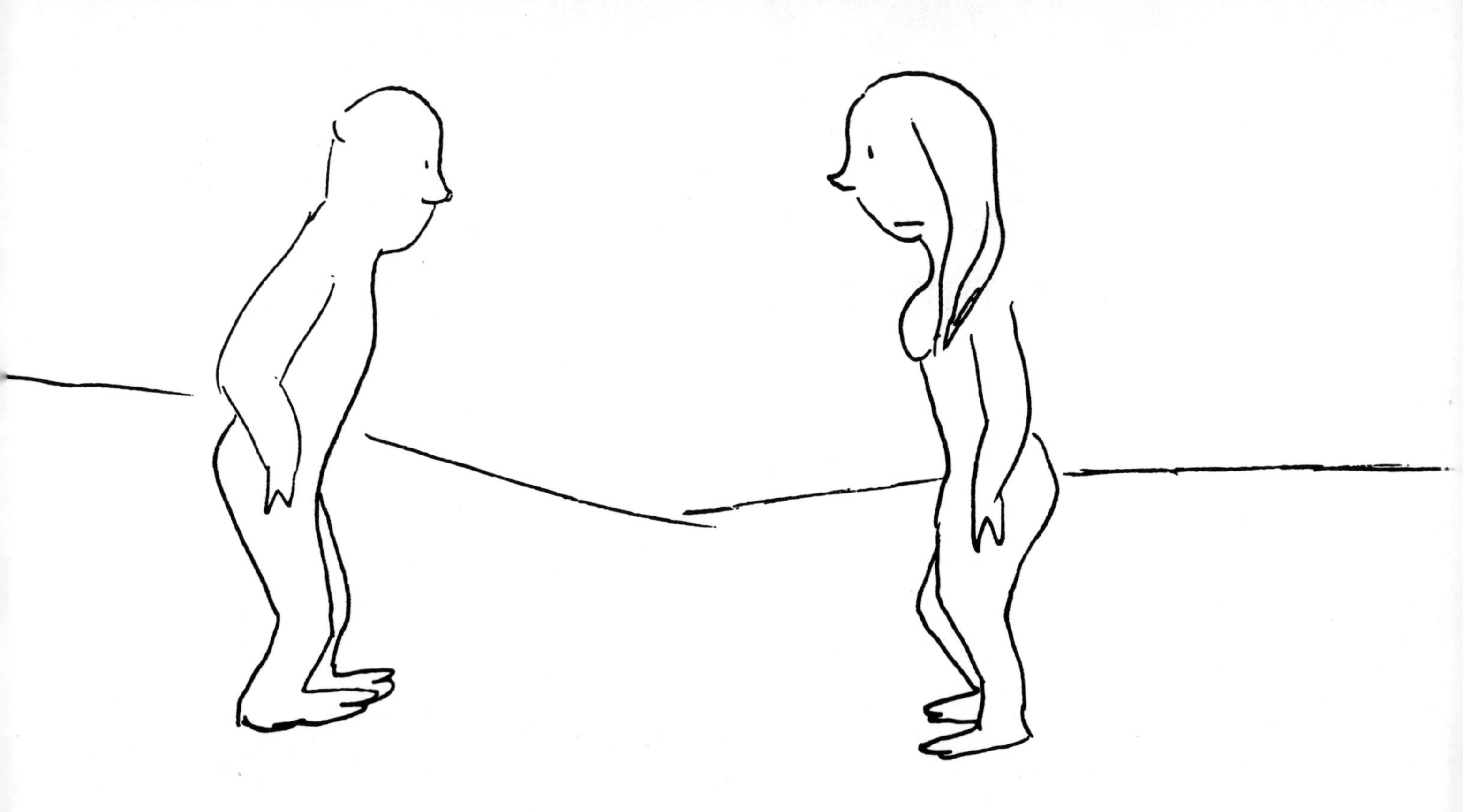

ONE DAY A YOUNG GIRL WHO HAD NEVER
SEEN A FLOWER CHANCED TO COME
UPON THE LAST ONE IN THE WORLD

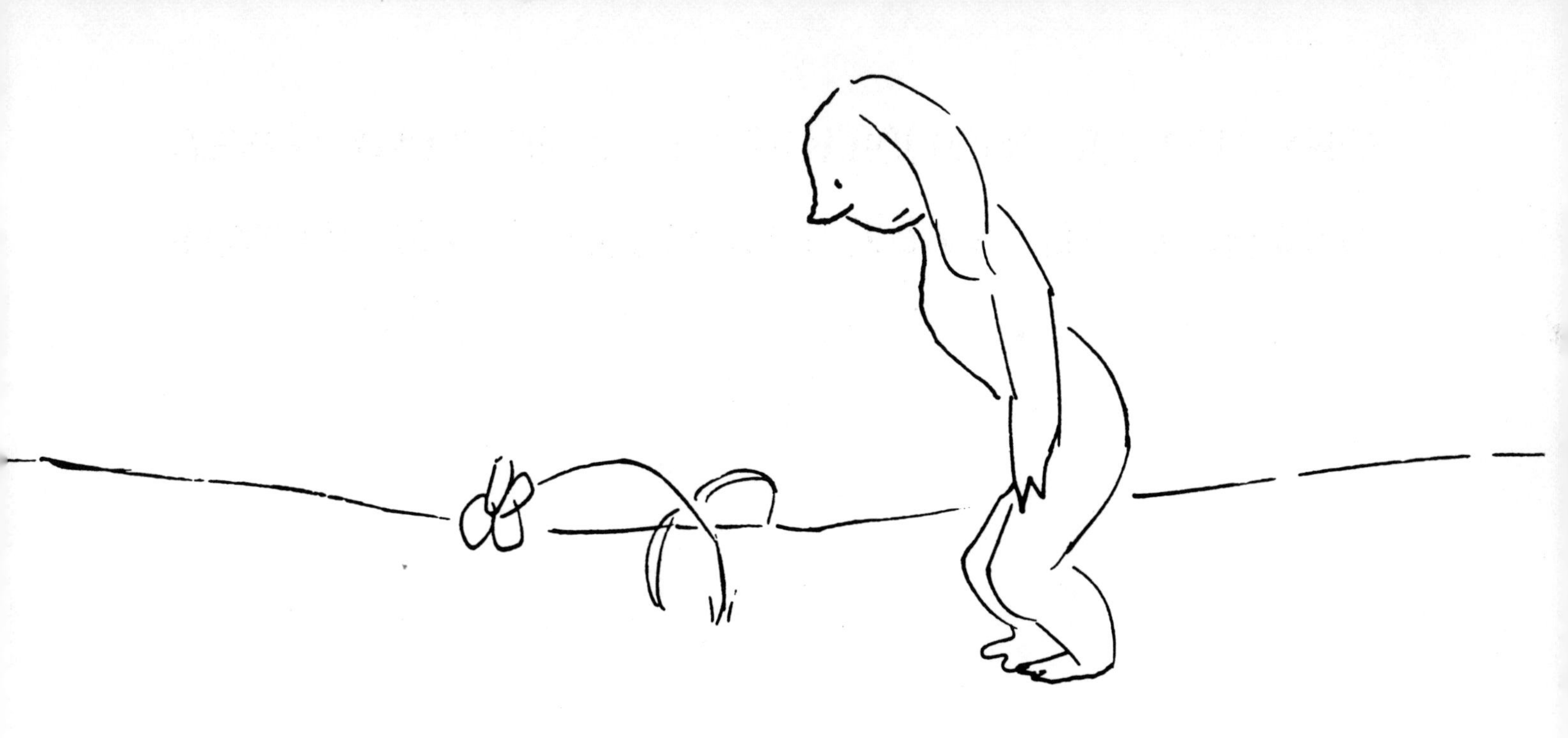

SHE TOLD THE OTHER HUMAN BEINGS
THAT THE LAST FLOWER WAS DYING

THE ONLY ONE WHO PAID ANY ATTENTION
TO HER WAS A YOUNG MAN SHE
FOUND WANDERING ABOUT

TOGETHER THE YOUNG MAN AND THE GIRL
NURTURED THE FLOWER AND IT BEGAN
TO LIVE AGAIN

ONE DAY A BEE VISITED THE FLOWER,

AND A HUMMINGBIRD

BEFORE LONG THERE WERE TWO FLOWERS, AND THEN FOUR, AND THEN A GREAT MANY

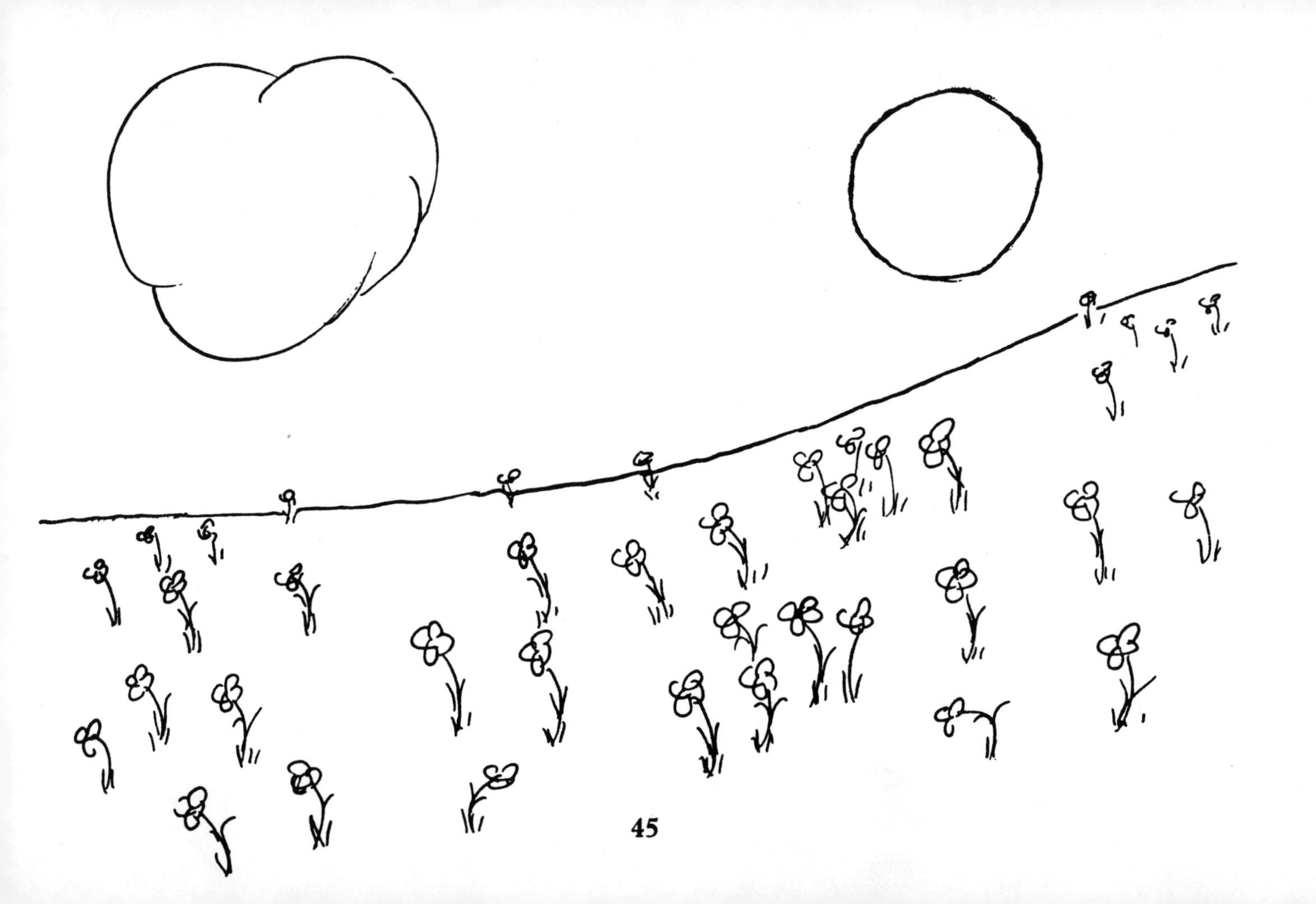

GROVES AND FORESTS FLOURISHED AGAIN

THE YOUNG GIRL BEGAN TO TAKE AN INTEREST IN HOW SHE LOOKED

THE YOUNG MAN DISCOVERED THAT
TOUCHING THE GIRL WAS PLEASURABLE

LOVE WAS REBORN INTO THE WORLD

THEIR CHILDREN GREW UP STRONG AND HEALTHY
AND LEARNED TO RUN AND LAUGH

DOGS CAME OUT OF THEIR EXILE

THE YOUNG MAN DISCOVERED, BY PUTTING ONE STONE UPON ANOTHER, HOW TO BUILD A SHELTER

PRETTY SOON EVERYBODY WAS BUILDING SHELTERS

TOWNS, CITIES, AND VILLAGES SPRANG UP

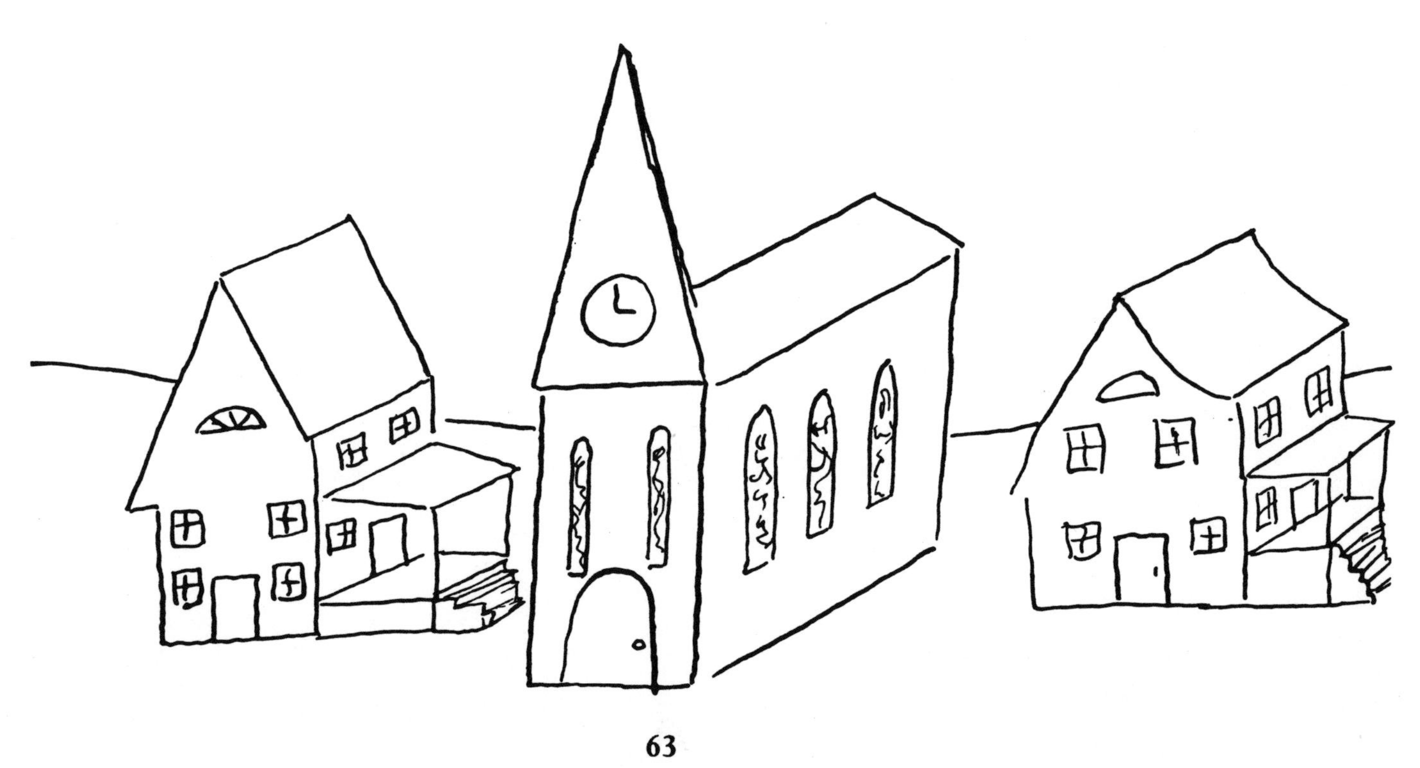

SONG CAME BACK INTO THE WORLD

AND TROUBADOURS AND JUGGLERS

AND TAILORS AND COBBLERS

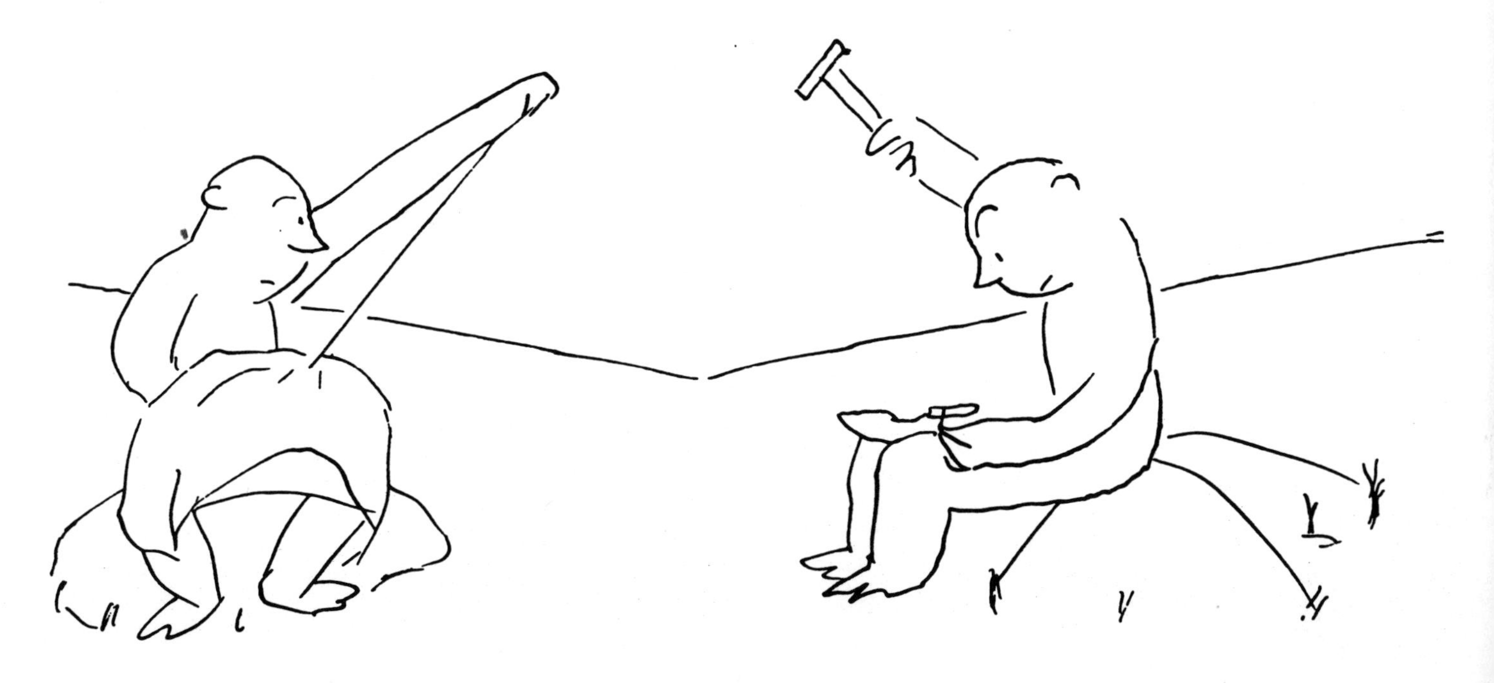

AND PAINTERS AND POETS

AND SCULPTORS AND WHEELWRIGHTS

AND SOLDIERS

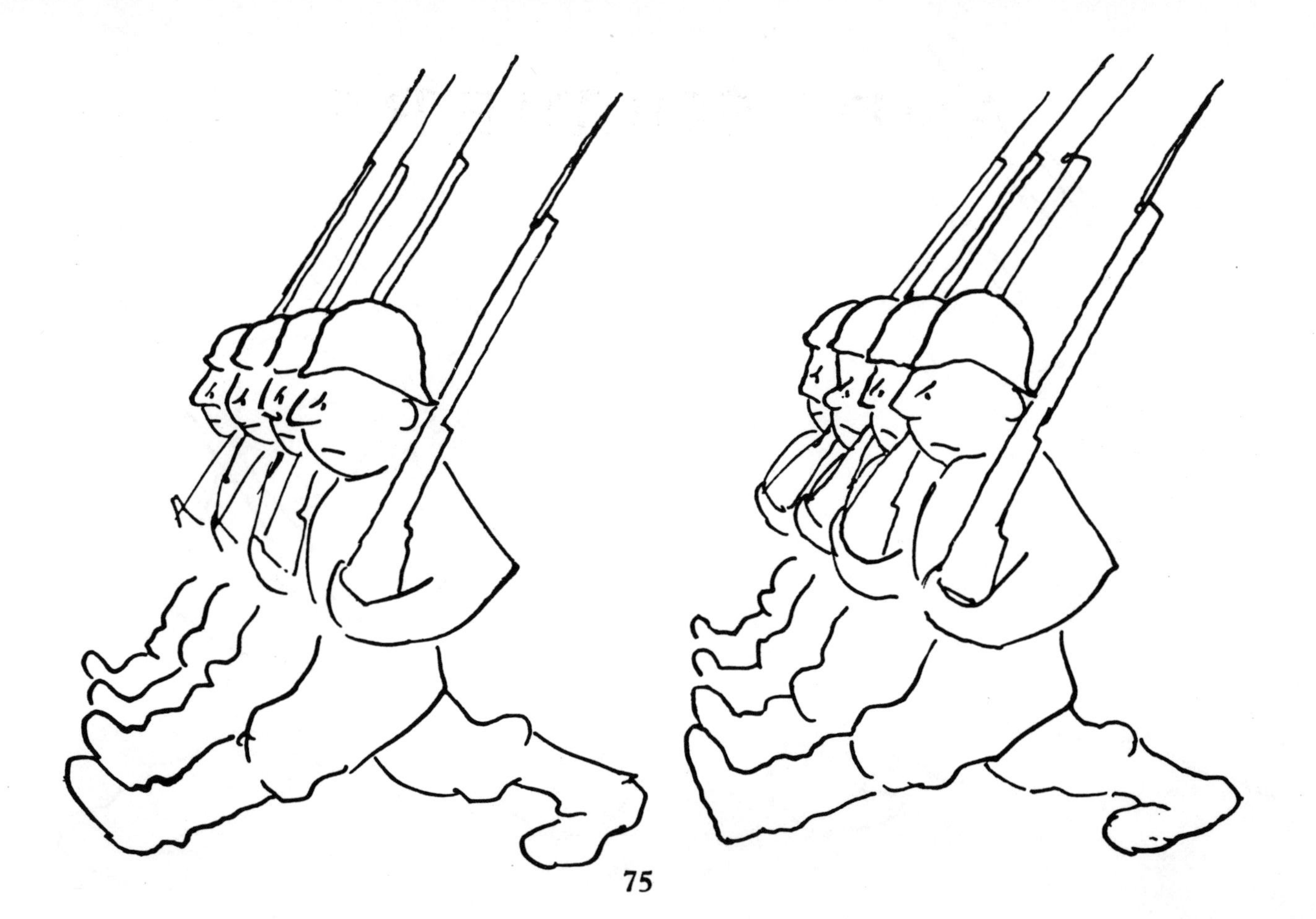

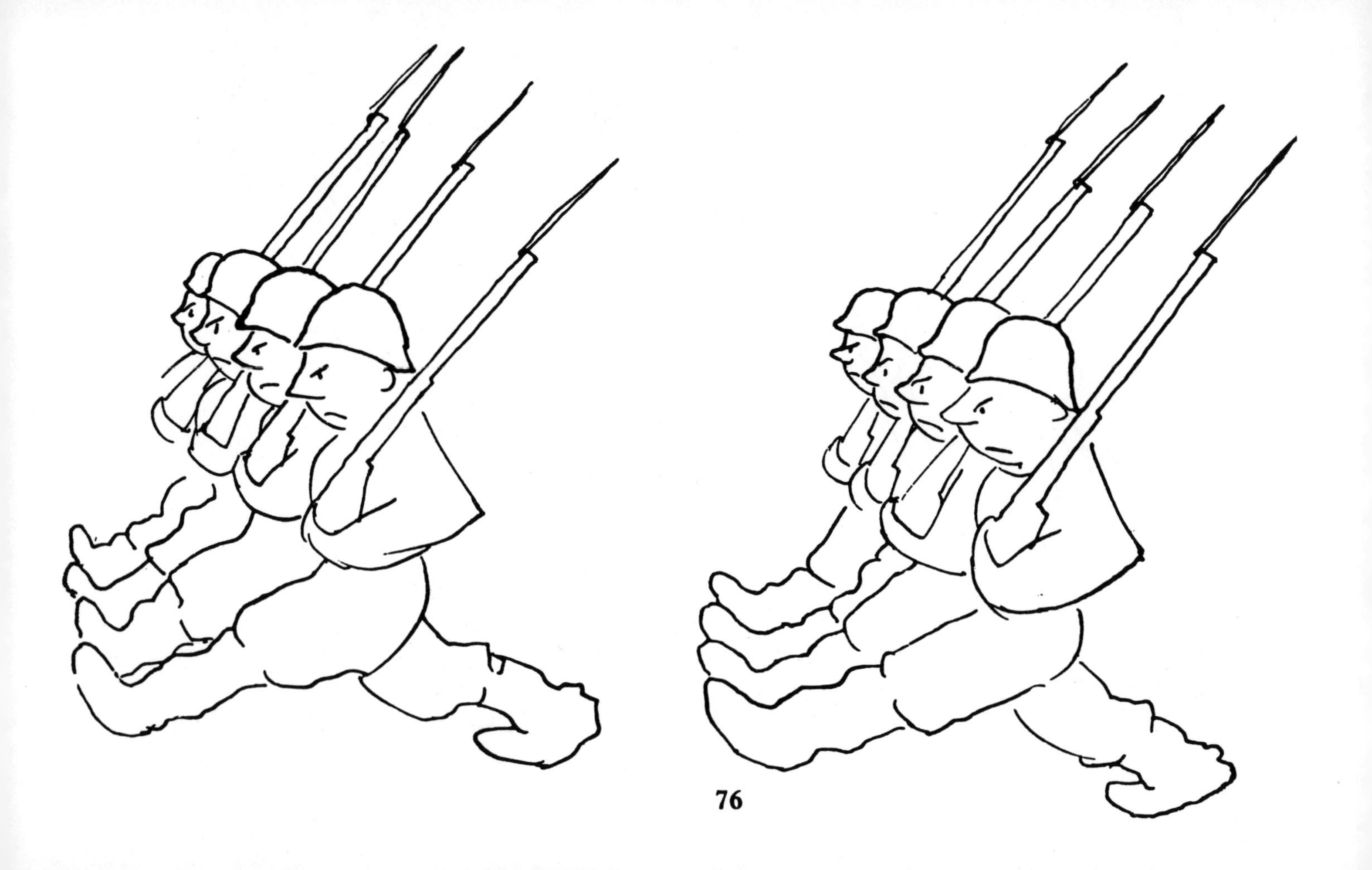

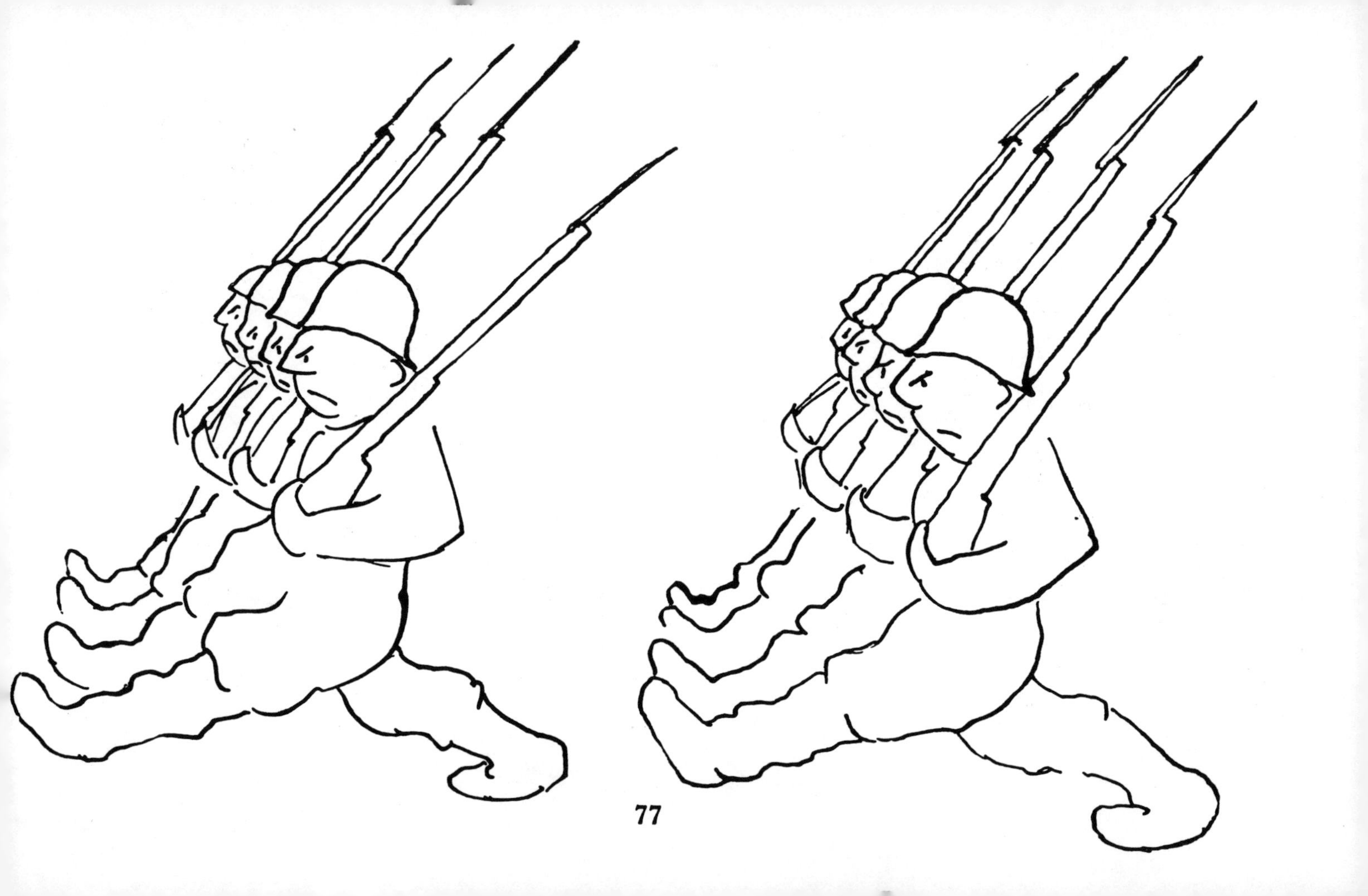

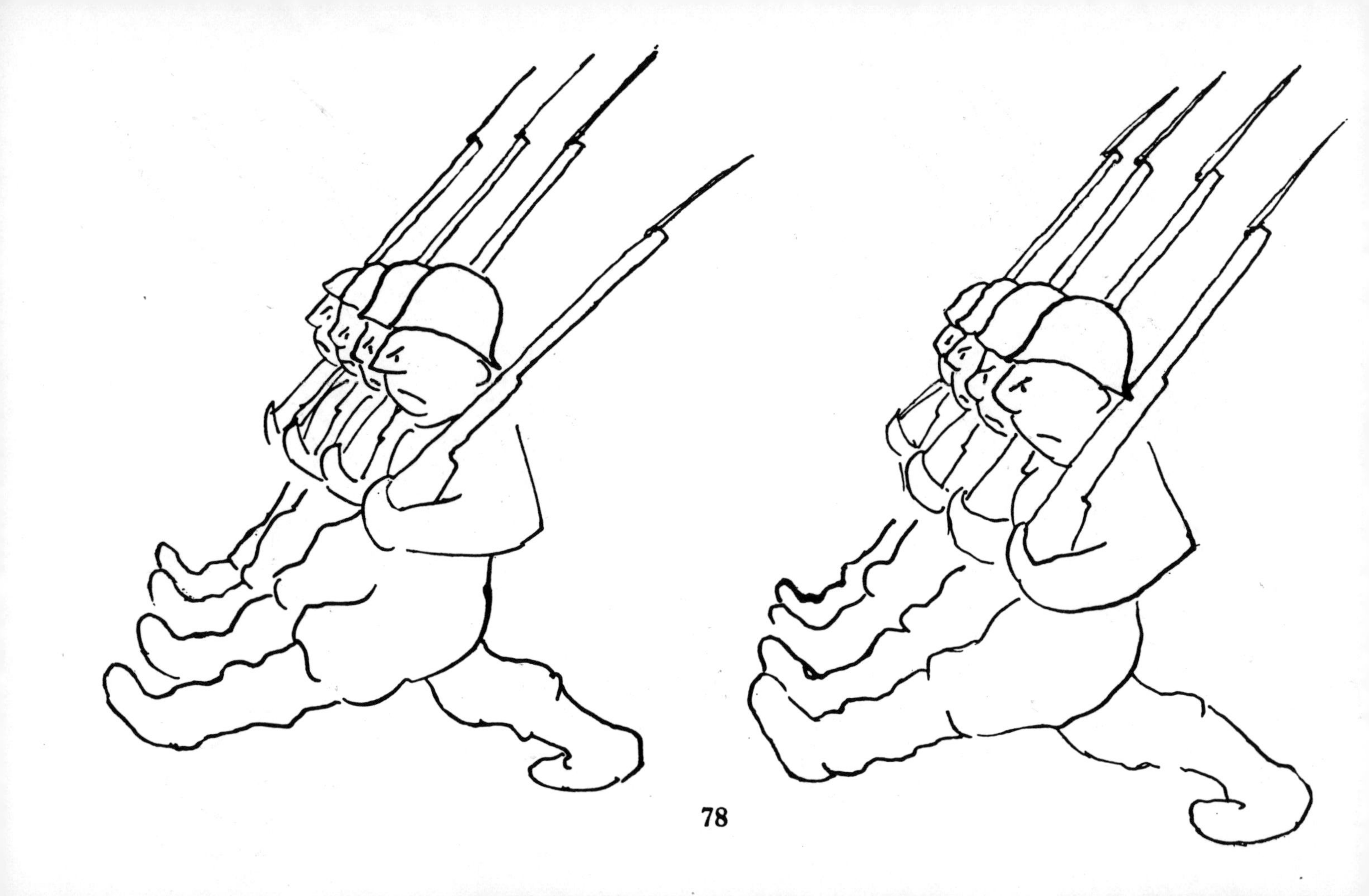

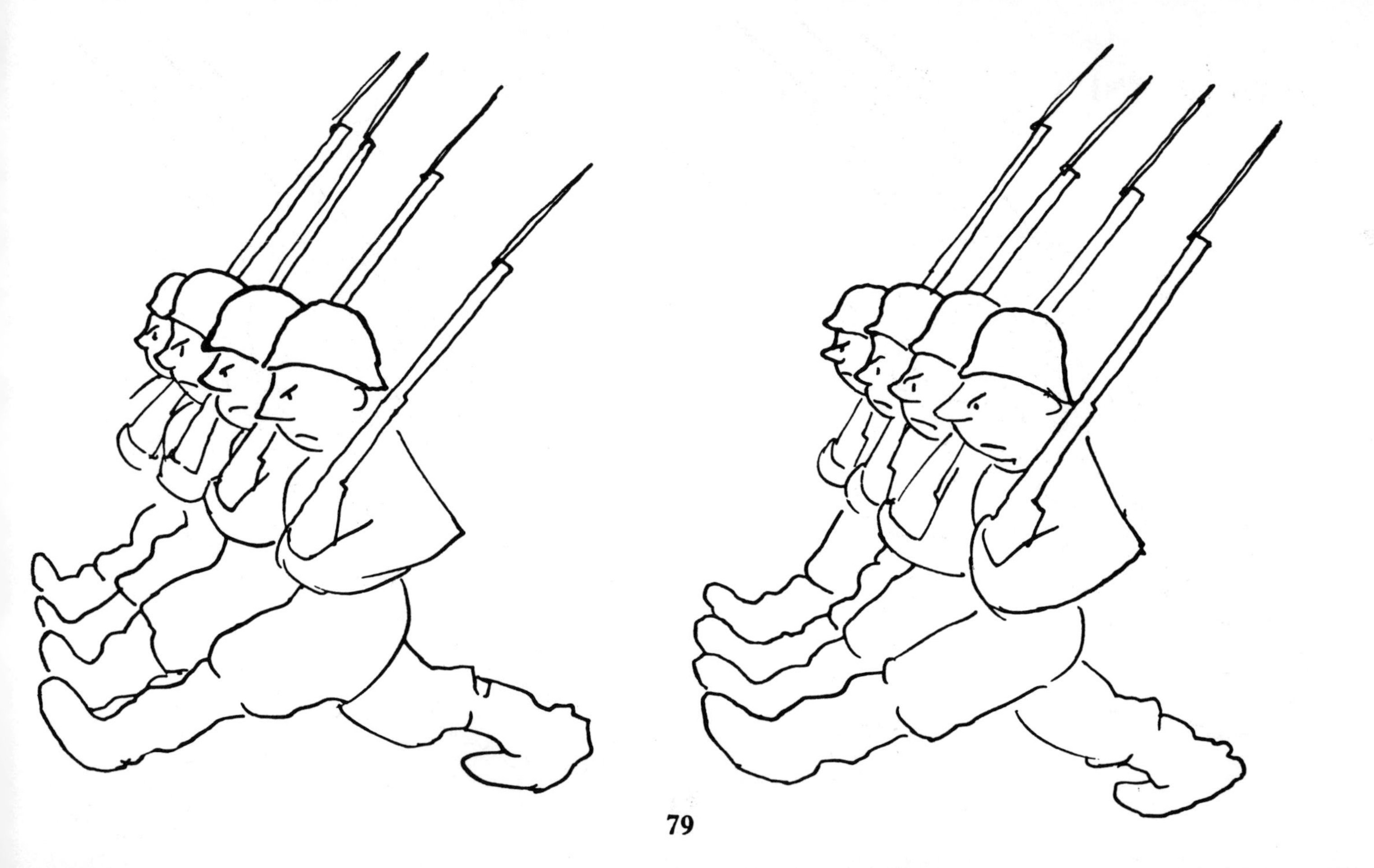

AND LIEUTENANTS AND CAPTAINS

AND GENERALS AND MAJOR-GENERALS

AND LIBERATORS

SOME PEOPLE WENT ONE PLACE TO LIVE,
AND SOME ANOTHER

BEFORE LONG, THOSE WHO WENT TO LIVE IN THE VALLEYS WISHED THEY HAD GONE TO LIVE IN THE HILLS

AND THOSE WHO HAD GONE TO LIVE IN THE HILLS

WISHED THEY HAD GONE TO LIVE IN THE VALLEYS

THE LIBERATORS, UNDER THE GUIDANCE OF GOD,

SET FIRE TO THE DISCONTENT

SO PRESENTLY THE WORLD WAS AT WAR AGAIN

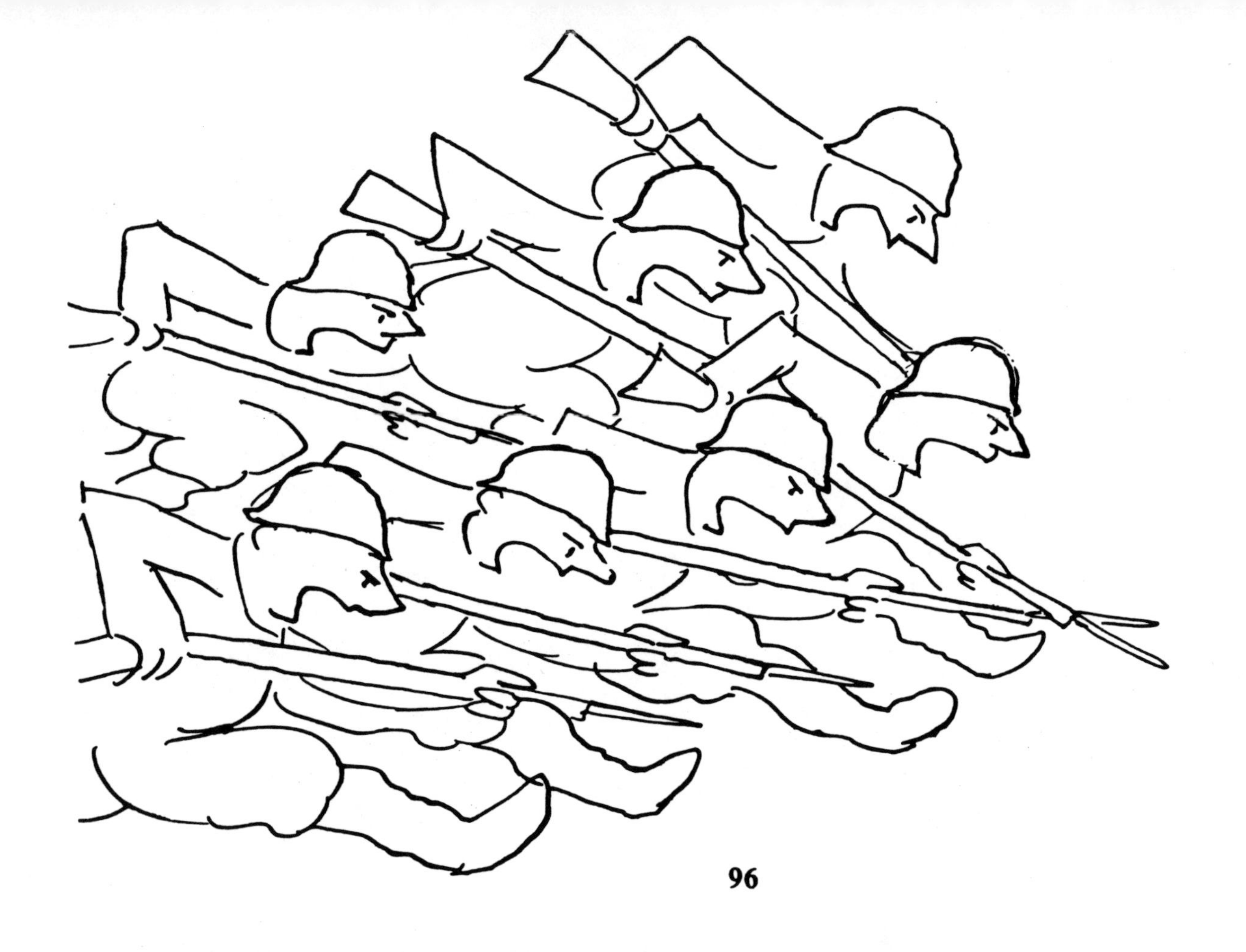

THIS TIME THE DESTRUCTION WAS SO COMPLETE...

THAT NOTHING AT ALL WAS LEFT IN THE WORLD

EXCEPT ONE MAN

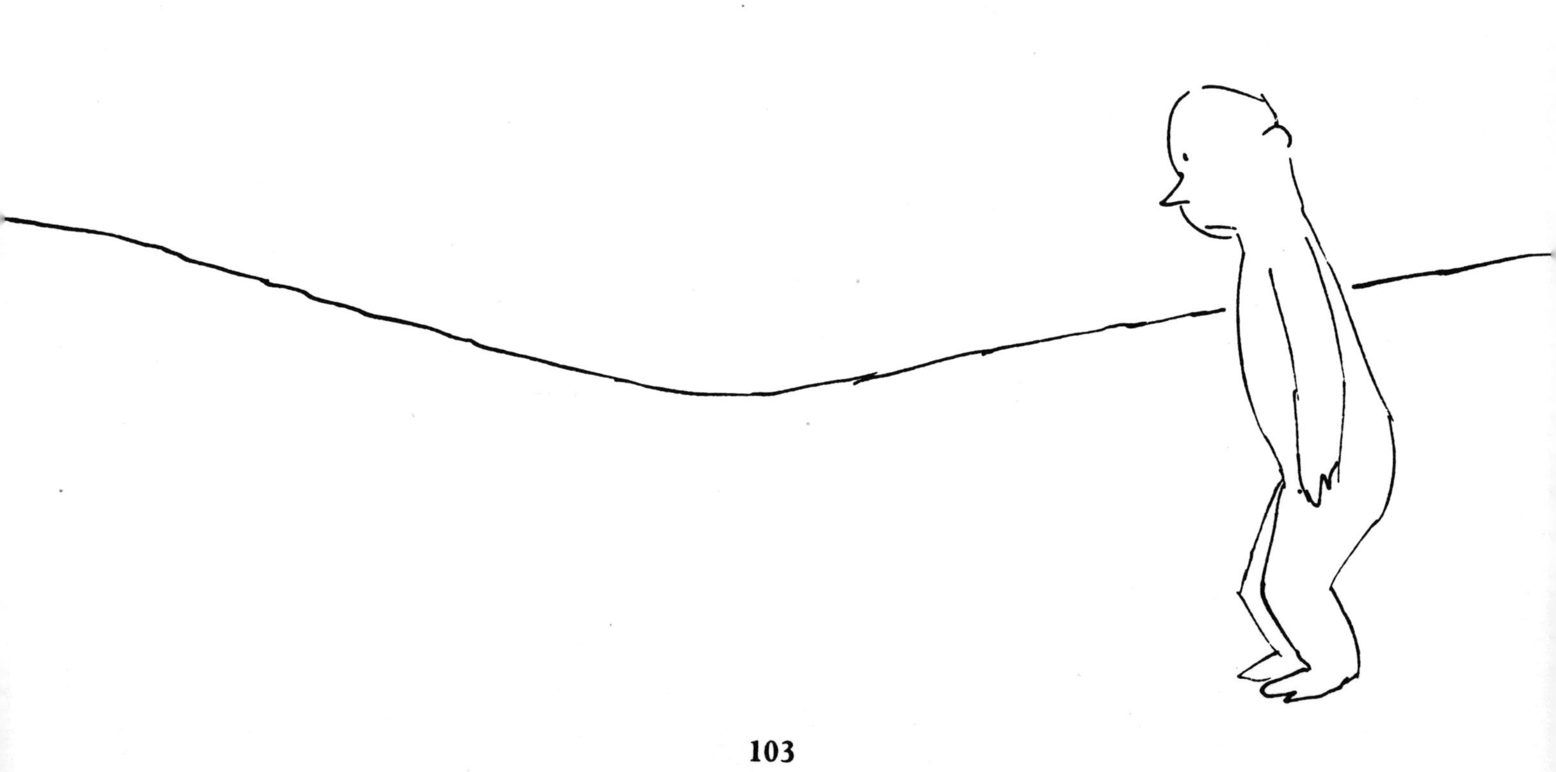

AND ONE WOMAN

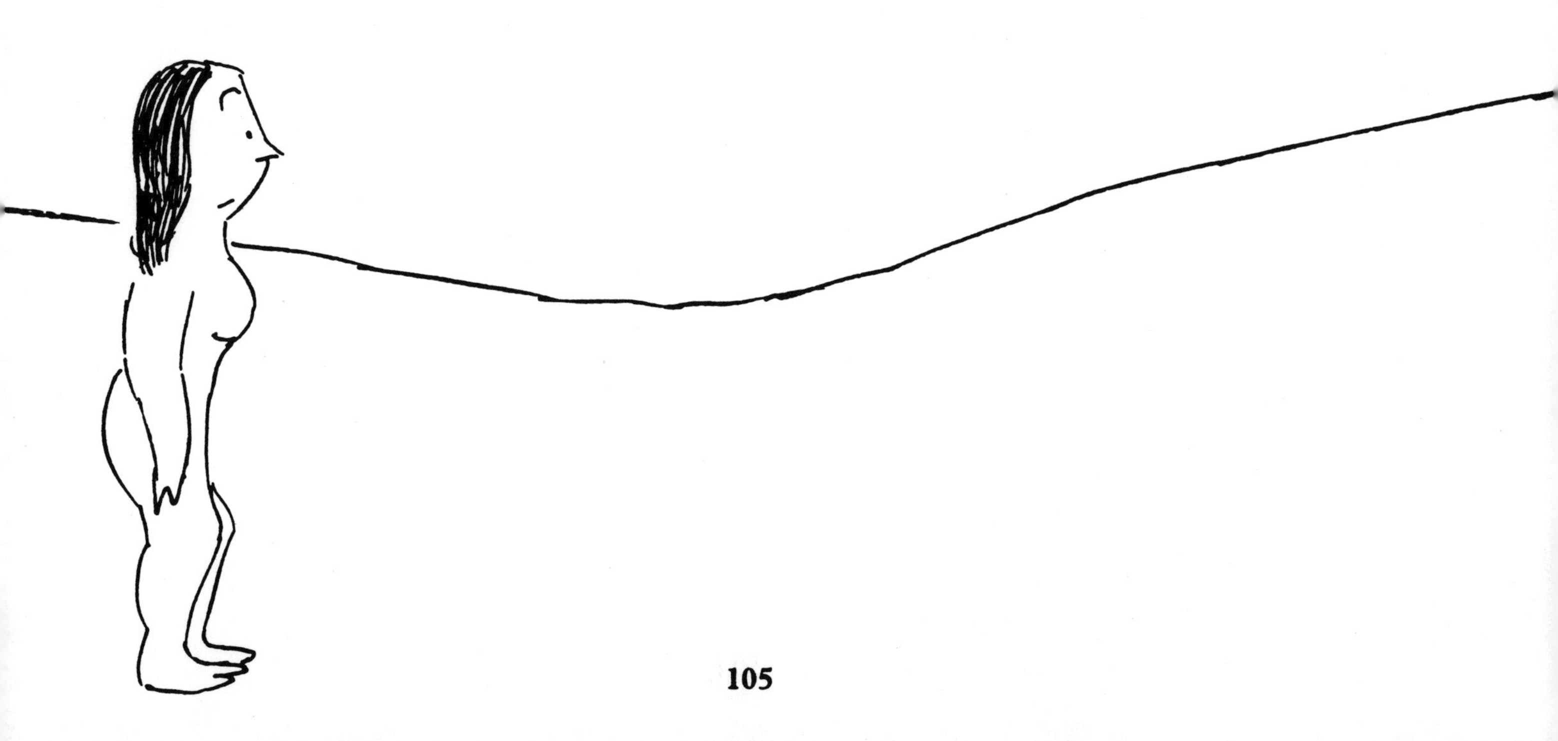

AND ONE FLOWER